KT-393-689

Story Of The
THREE LITTLE KITTENS

MOTHER CAT

TIM

YELLOW MITTENS

BLUE MITTENS

TOPSY

TIPSY

RED MITTENS

PIE

Illustrated by

Tom and Blonnie Holmes

IT'S FUN
TO READ ALONG

Here's what you do—

These pictures are some of the characters and things the story tells about. Let the child to whom you are reading SEE and SAY them.

Then, as you read the story text and come to a picture instead of a word, pause and point to the picture for your listener to SEE and SAY.

You'll be amazed at how quickly children catch on and enjoy participating in the story-telling.

ISBN 0 86163-809-3

Copyright © 1984 Award Publications
This edition first published 1995

Published by Award Publications Limited,
27 Longford Street, London NW1 3DZ

Printed in Belgium

Once there were **3** little  named Tipsy, Topsy, and Tim. They lived with their  in a wee tiny  on a  .

One day a  came from their grandmother. In the  was a  for  , a  for  and a  and pair of  for  .

The  put on their new clothes, and didn't they look grand!  cat said, "I'll make brand new  for all of you."

She finished them that very week:  for Tipsy, for Topsy, and

 for Tim. The  were very happy and proud as Punch of their new ⟨mittens⟩.

They wore them day in and day out, but one day they came to ⟨mother cat⟩ with ⟨tears⟩ in their ⟨eyes⟩. "We lost our ⟨mittens⟩," they sobbed. "Oh dear, whatever shall we do?"

was busy making a 🥧. She turned around quickly, and scolded, "Lost your you naughty 🐱s!

Then you shall have no  ."

The 🐱🐱🐱 wiped their 👀 with their 🐾🐾 and went to look for their 🧤 . They asked 🐔

if she had seen their ,
and next they asked the
playful  if he had
carried them away.

"Cluck," said . "No,
I did not see your ."

"Bow, wow! No!" barked the
playful . "I did not
carry away your ."

The  looked on top
of their s and under

their 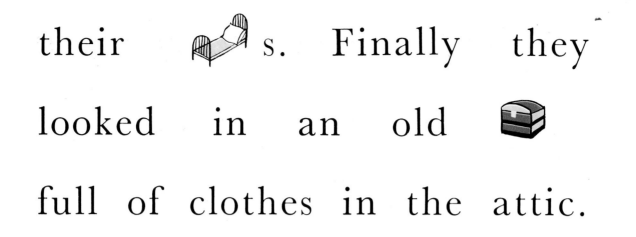s. Finally they

looked in an old

full of clothes in the attic.

"I don't see how they could be in this  ," said  .

"We haven't been in the attic for weeks."

 said, "We haven't been anywhere except the woods to pick  for  's  ."

"And that's just where they are!" squealed  .

"They're hanging on the

. Don't you remember we had to take them off in order to pick the ?"

The hurried to the . Sure enough, there were the

hanging from the  .
The 🐱 🐱 🐱 put them on
and ran home to 🐱 .
She was so glad they
had found the 🧤 that
she gave them the 🥧 .

"It's the best  I have ever eaten," said 🐱.

"It's the juiciest  I have ever eaten," said 🐱.

"But look at our 🧤," said 🐱.

The  ran to
and showed her their sticky
messy . "You naughty
s!" scolded .

So again the 3 little 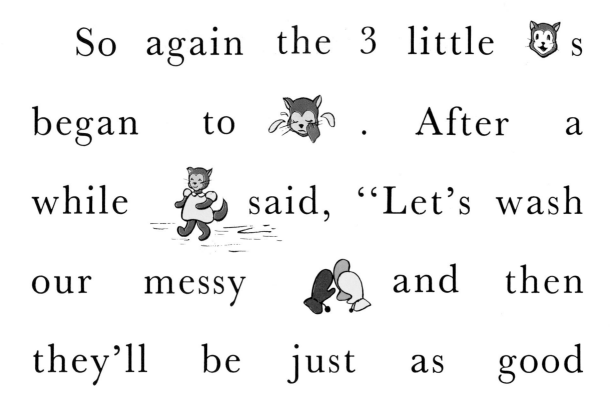s began to 🐱. After a while 🐱 said, "Let's wash our messy 🧤 and then they'll be just as good as new!"

ran to get the 🧼 .

ran for the wash🪣 ,

brought out the

🐾🐾🐾🐾 and the 🧺 .

They filled the 🪣 with

water and made lots of

🧼 suds. Then they threw

in the 🧤 and scrubbed

and scrubbed and

scrubbed until the 🫐

stain had disappeared.

Then the s hung their on the clothes line to dry. Soon they were soft and fluffy and dry.

The  ran to  . She smiled at  wearing her blue  , and at Topsy with her red  and at  with his bright yellow  . She said to

them happily, "You are the best s in all the . Now let's all be very quiet, because I smell a close by."

The 3 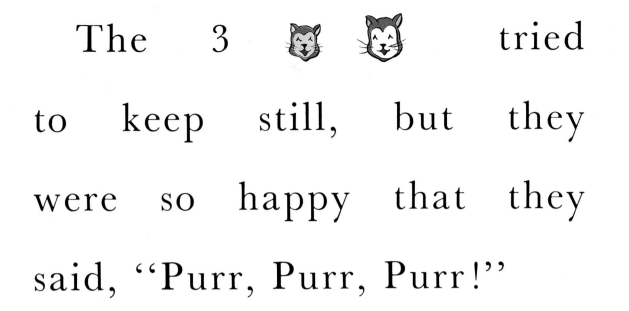 tried to keep still, but they were so happy that they said, "Purr, Purr, Purr!"

THE THREE LITTLE KITTENS

*Here is a poem about the Three Little Kittens
for you to read and learn.*

Three little kittens lost their mittens,
      And they began to cry.
"Oh, Mother dear, we sadly fear
      Our mittens we have lost."

"What! Lost your mittens?
      You naughty kittens!
Then you shall have no pie."
      "Me-ow, me-ow, me-ow, me-ow."

The three little kittens
      found their mittens,
      And they began to cry,
"Oh, Mother dear, see here, see here,
      Our mittens we have found!"

"What! Found your mittens?
        You good little kittens!
Then you shall have some pie."
        Purr-purr-purr-purr!

The three little kittens
        put on their mittens,
        And soon ate up the pie;
"Oh, Mother dear, we greatly fear
        That we have soiled our mittens."

"Soiled your mittens!
        You naughty kittens!"
Then they began to sigh,
        "Mi-ew, mi-ew, mi-ew, mi-ew."

The three little kittens
        washed their mittens,
        And hung them up to dry:
"Oh, Mother dear, look here, look here!
        See, we have washed our mittens."

"Washed your mittens!
        You clever kittens!
But I smell a rat close by.
    Hush! Hush!"
        "Mee-ow, mee-ow,
        We smell a rat close by."